A LIFT-THE-FLAP BOOK

CORDUROY'S CHRISTMAS

BASED ON THE CHARACTER BY DON FREEMAN

STORY BY B. G. HENNESSY

PICTURES BY LISA McCUE

A SCHOLASTIC EDITION

Corduroy loves Christmas.
There are so many things to do.

First Corduroy trims his Christmas tree.
But where is the angel for the top of the tree?

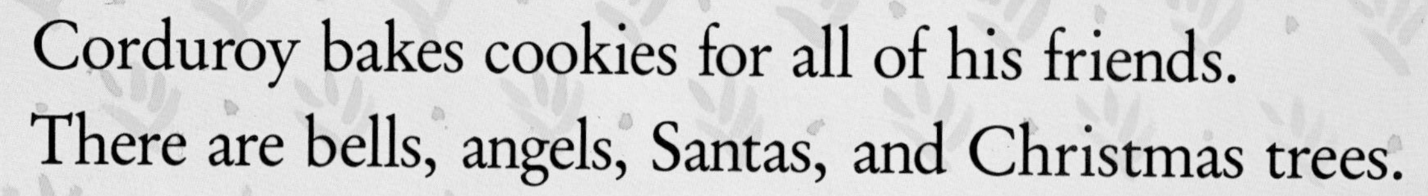

Corduroy bakes cookies for all of his friends.
There are bells, angels, Santas, and Christmas trees.

Mmmmmmm! This batch is done.
Better take them out of the oven, Corduroy!

TEA
SUGAR
FLO
LISA MCCUE
1992

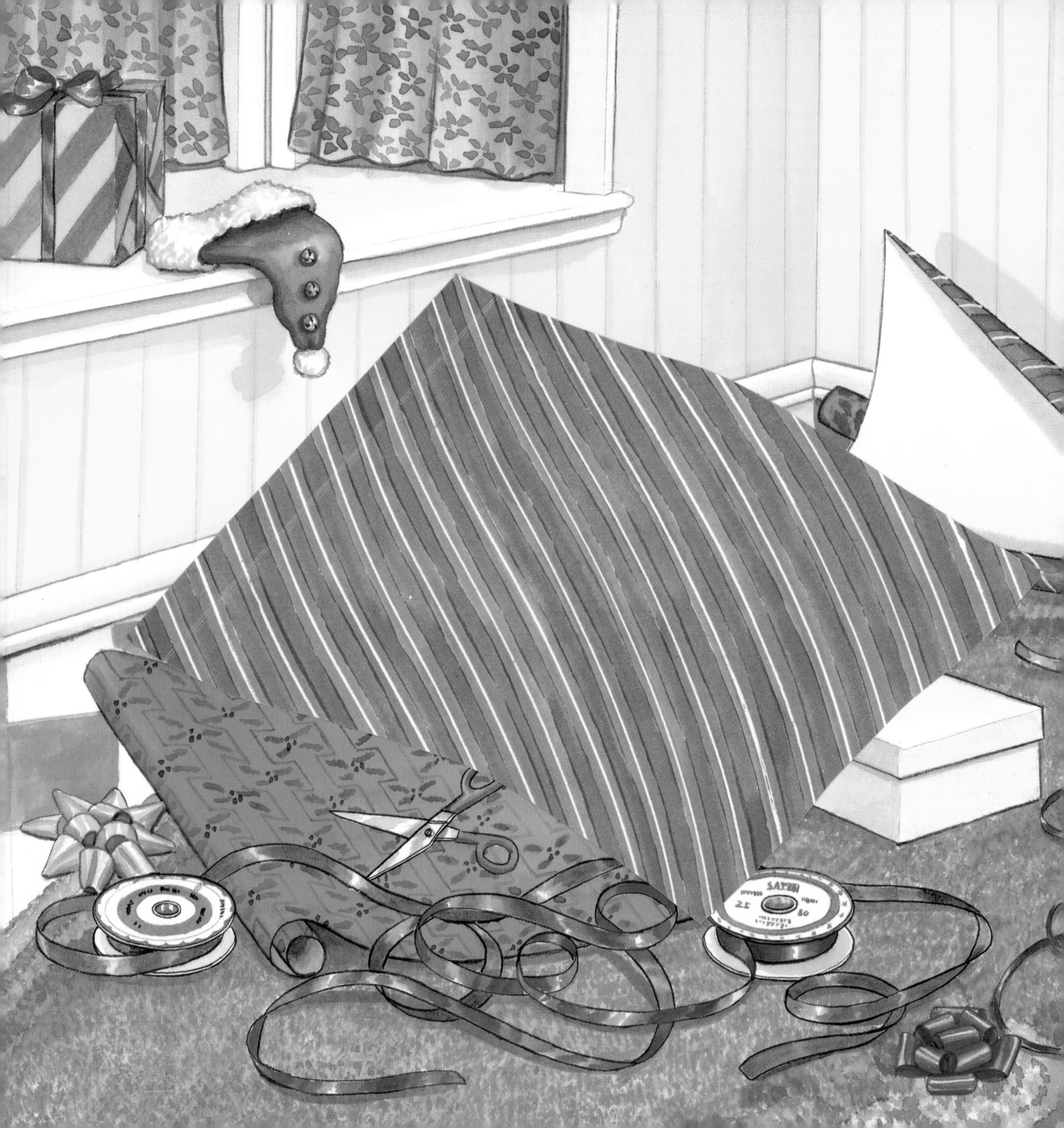
SATIN
25
80

Now it's time to wrap the presents.
Corduroy gets out the wrapping paper,
tape, ribbons, and scissors.

Oops—where is Corduroy?

Corduroy Bear
Santa Claus
North Pole

Corduroy has written his letter to Santa.
He is going to send it to the North Pole.

Look! Outside it has started to snow.

Corduroy and his friends are going caroling.
But which one is Corduroy?

It's Christmas Eve. Corduroy has hung up his stocking and left a note for Santa. Now he is fast asleep.

Listen! Is that someone on the roof?

For Santa
Merry
Christmas
Corduroy

It's Christmas morning!
Look at all the presents Santa
brought for Corduroy!

Merry Christmas, Corduroy!

DON FREEMAN was born in San Diego, California, and moved to New York City to study art, making his living as a jazz trumpeter. With the loss of his trumpet on a subway train, Mr. Freeman turned his talents to art full-time. In the 1940s, he began writing and illustrating children's books. His many popular titles include *Corduroy*, *A Pocket for Corduroy*, *Beady Bear*, *Dandelion*, *Mop Top*, and *Norman the Doorman.*

LISA McCUE was born in Tappan, New York, and has illustrated more than 75 books, including *Corduroy's Toys*, *Corduroy's Day*, and *Corduroy On the Go.* She lives in Bethlehem, Pennsylvania, with her husband and their new baby.

A SCHOLASTIC EDITION
ISBN 0-590-46450-7

 Published by Scholastic Inc.,
730 Broadway, New York, NY 10003,
by arrangement with Viking Penguin,
a division of Penguin Books USA Inc.

12 11 10 9 8 7 6 5 4 3 2 1   3 4 5 6 7 8/9

Printed in Singapore

First Scholastic printing, November 1993